MAMA'S BABY & DADDY'S BABY TOO

Written by: Destini Belton

Illustrated by: Adua Hernandez

Hi

My name is _____

and I like to read.

Visit iamurdestini.com to explore more of the author's work, social media, products & services.

Published by Play Your Cards Right LLC

1617 3rd avenue Po Box 286364

All rights reserved, including the right of reproduction in whole or in part in any form.
Copyright © 2021 Play Your Cards Right

4/27/2021

www.iamurdestini.com

First Edition

The author asserts the moral right under the Copyright, Designs and Patents Act of 1988 to be identified as the author of this work.
All rights reserved. No part of this publication may be reproduced, stored in a retrieval system or transmitted, in any form by any means without the prior consent of the author, nor be otherwise circulated in any form of binding or cover other than that with which it is published and without a similar condition being imposed
on the subsequent purchaser.

All rights reserved.

Library of Congress Control Number: 2021907977

ISBN: 978-1-7370723-0-0 hardback

ISBN: 978-1-7370723-1-7 paperback

ISBN: 978-1-7370723-2-4 ebook

Dedicated to my incredibly unique and talented three beautiful children Elana, Eric Jr., and Anthony Lowe. Thank you for giving my life a purposeful meaning. You three fill me with overwhelming amounts of gratitude, joy, peace, and love since the day I laid my eyes on your adorable faces. Secondly my beloved grandmother, Delores V. Atkinson, who made single parenting a supernatural power. Rest in paradise "Dot". Thank you for your unconditional love. My life's journey has been inspired by my loving, caring, admirable and well-respected parents Althea, and Tony Belton. Thank you for being an exception to the rule. Making it last through the good, bad, ugly, saved, and holy. You are a true epitome of black love, resilience, and sacrifice. Finally, I would like to acknowledge my partner in love, Eric A. Lowe. Thank you for blessing me with our three most precious gifts GOD designed and crafted perfectly for us. You have taught me to embrace my flaws, acknowledge my worth and own my greatness. Thank you for holding my hand through it all.

Aren't we blessed to have **mommy** and **DADDY** both **?!**

They are always here when we need them the most.
Mommy is an expert in bathing,

cleaning, grooming and singing

But DADDY tells the best jokes

Mommy likes to cuddle and read until we are fast asleep,

DADDY makes us laugh and smile by bringing us snacks and treats,

Mommy makes sure we have vegetables with dinner

She even packs fruits for school and Daycare

With both of them by our side we feel extremely loved and protected

Oh what would I do without them two

They sacrifice their lives so we aren't neglected

Does it surprise you DADDY cooks the most?!

And does all the laundry, you should smell our clothes (ahhhhhhh)?

Mommy swiffers dusts and organizes the house.

She even goes food shopping and takes us to church.

Guess who buys our clothes?

Mommy styles us the best.

And picks out the sneakers ?

DADDY'S an expert at that.

Or taught us how to pray before we begin eating !?

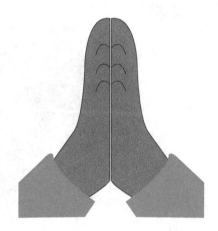

Mommy and DADDY works as a team. Can you believe it ?

To ensure our happiness , love and self esteem

What would we do without you working side by side?

Just for the family.

That's a question we wouldn't want to answer

It feels so good when we are together.

See you later

Never goodbye

Mommy is irreplaceable

And DADDY'S love cannot be denied.

ABOUT THE AUTHOR

Destini S. Belton, daughter of Tony And Althea Belton, is a Spanish Harlem native cultivated and bred in the heart of New York City. Her "East Harlem" combined with "South Bronx" upbringing introduced her to the multi layered socioeconomic cultural differences that vary distinctively. Destini's upbringings consist of but are not limited to New York City Housing Association (NYCHA'S) Claremont Housing free lunches and cookouts, to SAT prep classes at Fordham University, East River/Wilson Housing Family Day, Barry University's dorm life, Bloomberg LP's Randall's Island festivities and more. Early on she survived domestic violence, experienced emotional, verbal, mental/physical abuse and witnessed mental health, drug addiction and poverty woes struck upon her close family members and neighbors within the community; yet her determination and will to survive silenced her fear to prevail. Upon the brink of survival, she gained experiences which prepared her for the multi-faceted journey ahead. Her exposure to variations of class, religious

beliefs, education, access, and opportunity enlightened a conscious awareness heightened overtime. Although Destini was impacted directly from the residue of Jim Crow, systemic racism, mass incarceration, and poverty, the foundation laid by her parents encouraged her to strive for success despite the inevitable roadblocks inserted to disrupt the acceleration of impoverished, low income and black/brown communities. With the support of Destini's mother Althea, during her childhood she built a résumé in acting. Destini appeared as extras in movies such as: "Objects of my Affection" and "Stepmom." In addition, she also appeared in school textbooks and bus stop ads as a child model, starred in plays like "Alice in Wonderland" (while attending a professional acting class at age 7) playing "The Queen of Hearts", and perfected her vocal capabilities, piano and dance skills (ethnic, jazz and modern) at the well renowned Harlem School of the Arts.

The skills attained broadened her horizons which instilled a passion for performing arts and entertainment. As a seventh-grade student at St. Joseph's of Yorkville, she developed and adapted a gift of poetry writing that ignited her passion for writing/songwriting. Throughout high school while studying at the prestigious Cardinal Spellman, she wrote "R&B" songs religiously (specifically during Global 101 class freshman year and throughout the years), took on leadership roles like Class Senator, African American Club Secretary and Dance Club Choreographer/President.

After graduating in June 2005, Destini shortly after gained her independence accepting an offer at Barry university, nearly 18 hours and 1281 miles away from home. As early as 17 years old, Destini was exposed to even more cultural diversity, educational opportunities and privileged resources which were unimaginably at her fingertips. After an eventful, memorable, and life-changing year and a half in college, she returned home to discover adulthood in its truest form. Due to financial inequities, Destini hit the ground running in early 2007 no longer able to attend Barry nor The City University Of New York (CUNY). Determined to acquire skills necessary in New York City's competitive job market, she worked in several industries such as entertainment, finance, emergency services, hospitality, and currently health care. Aside from being a formally certified "Emergency Medical Technician" (EMT-Basic), and acquiring a New York "Mixology" license, all the professional experiences and skills inherited prepared her to perform adequately, effectively, and tenaciously in almost any arena. Not to mention her ability to write songs, studio record and accolade received for a past performance during the "Faces in the Crowd" competition (which she landed FIRST place) at SOB's "Sounds of Brazil", Destini recently curated "Play Your Cards Right" Fall of 2018 (reinventing her creative space), a production company to provoke cultural awareness through conversation, writing and entertainment. Her drive to create is embodied in the passion she possesses, determination to thrive and desire to shift the culture's narrative.

At the age of 26, April 15th, 2014, Destini gave birth to her daughter and first-born child, Elana Lowe. Elana took priority in her everyday tasks and duties, putting many of her dreams and aspirations on hold. Although the responsibility of motherhood seemed overwhelmingly demanding, the fulfillment and joy of having such a perfect, beautiful, and pure human being made it all worth it. In 2017, three years later, God spoke and said, "Let there be two!" On September 5th, 2017 Destini gave birth to a set of fraternal twin boys who inspire her tremendously (especially two young black boys living in a society where they are proven to be threats). Creating pathways for their success provides a sense of inspiration necessary to excel. All the achievements, struggles, wins and losses no longer hold weight due to a bigger plan God set in place for her destiny.

Today Destini's goal is to prioritize motherhood while continuing to model success through her own behaviors and actions. She is no longer waiting for the validation of others to determine her moves, nor is she allowing the projection of fears to resonate with her decision making. The goal is to be the change she wants to see. Destini wants to encourage others to educate themselves and understand education starts at home. Over the past year COVID-19 has taken over 500,00 lives in the United States. One of those lives included Destini's 89-year-old maternal grandmother, Delores Virginia Atkinson, who is missed dearly. Despite the lives lost and irreplaceable heartache families face daily, she has gained new insight. Belton realizes tomorrow is not promised to anyone. Nothing in life is certain but death. Let us normalize cherishing every day, thanking GOD for HIS grace and each intricate breath. In closing, Destini is a daughter, sister, mother, Christian, author, entrepreneur, song/entertainment writer, artist, health coach, innovator and curator breaking the curse of generational poverty by any means necessary.

About Author- Edited by "Chasidy Forbes".

ELANA

Eric Jr.

Anthony

ERIC & ANTHONY

"Train up a child in the way he should go: and when he is old, he will not depart from it."
Proverbs 22:6

Single mothers are the EPITOME of superheroes. Your magic doesn't go unnoticed. The next book will be dedicated to all my single SUPERWOMEN. My grandmother, Delores Atkinson, whom shall rest in HIS peace, was a true example of a mother whose magic worked wonders on lives she touched.

CPSIA information can be obtained
at www.ICGtesting.com
Printed in the USA
BVHW011711260621
610449BV00013B/2737